S0-BBI-453

The Bus

By Ann Naumann
Illustrated by Susan Spellman

The bus takes us
to Grandma.

The bus takes us
to the zoo.

The bus takes us
to the beach.

The bus takes us to the mall.

**The bus takes us
to the park.**

The bus takes us to the library.

The bus takes us home!